Spelling Practice

A LAUGHING LOBSTER BOOK 978-1-913906-03-0

Published in Great Britain by Laughing Lobster
an imprint of Centum Publishing Ltd.
This edition published 2021.
1 3 5 7 9 10 8 6 4 2

Illustrations by Louise Gardner.

Laughing Lobster an imprint of Centum Publishing Ltd, 20 Devon Square,
Newton Abbot, Devon, TQ12 2HR, UK
books@centumpublishingltd.co.uk
LAUGHING LOBSTER AN IMPRINT OF CENTUM PUBLISHING
Limited Reg. No. 08497203

A CIP catalogue record for this book is available from the British Library.

Printed in China.

Answers are at the back of the book!

About this book

The activities in this book will help your child to practise and become more confident with spelling.

Practice and repetition are a tried and tested way for your child to learn to spell new words, but you can make the experience more fun by making a game out of the process. Here are some ideas to help you:

1. If you come across a new word together, encourage your child to pick out the letters. Can they think of any other words that start or finish with the same letter?

2. When you are out and about, ask your child to spell simple words that you see around you, such as the names of shops.

3. Play simple rhyming games with your child. For example: 'How many words can you find that sound the same as "boat" or "bike"?'

Before you start:

1. Find a quiet place for you and your child to work, preferably at a table.

2. Help your child to learn to hold a pencil correctly. This will make learning easier for them, and give them the confidence to form the letters of the words they are practising.

3. Always give your child plenty of praise and encouragement. They don't have to complete each page in one go. Stop or move onto another page if they get tired or distracted.

The alphabet

My name is Mia. Practise writing the letters of the alphabet with me by tracing over the dotted lines, then say each letter out loud. Now write the correct letter at the start of each word to finish spelling it out.

a — a pple

b — b all

c — c at

d — d og

e — e lephant

f — f ish

g — g irl

h — h en

i — i nsect

j — j am

k — k ite

l — l emon

The alphabet

Trace over the dotted lines to complete the letters.

m
m ouse

n
n ut

o
o range

p
p ear

q
q ueen

r
r abbit

s
s ock

t
t eddy

u
u mbrella

v
v iolin

w
w indow

x
x -ray

y
y acht

z
z ebra

Now write the correct letter at the start of each word to finish spelling it out.

4

Spelling time!

My name is Joe. We are learning to spell lots of different words at school. Help me to write the first letter of each word to finish spelling it out.

J_ug

E_gg

D_og

B_oat

b_ird

O_range

H_at

B_oy

How many words in the list above start with the letter 'b'?
Write them here.

....

Family fun

I love all the members of my family, especially Dudley the dog!

Woof!

Choose a letter to complete each word.

b g m s g d

__M__um

__d__ad

__b__rother

__s__ister

__G__randpa

__g__randma

Draw a picture of your family.

6

Animal word endings

My name is Poppy and this is Mops, my fluffy pet rabbit. I love animals! Help me to finish these animal words by writing in one of the letters below. Don't forget, some of the letters will be used more than once. Then draw lines to match each word with the correct animal.

x t d w g h

do_g_

fo_x_

rabbi_t_

ca_t_

fis_h_

bir_d_

co_w_

pi_g_

Animal sounds

Do you know what noises these animals make?
Finish each animal noise by writing a letter at
the start of each sound.

Use the letters listed below:

w t c o m s b

_m_oo

_m_eow

_t_weet

_c_luck

_o_ink

_s_queak

_w_oof

_b_aa

Vowels and consonants

My name is Noah and I am learning about vowels. The letters **a e i o u** are all vowels. All the other letters in the alphabet are called consonants. Write in the missing vowels to finish each word, then fill in the paint splats in the right colours.

or_a_nge

gre_e_n

p_i_nk

yell_o_w

bl_u_e

b_a_by

_a_pple

h_a_t

t_e_ddy

p_e_n

Vowels and consonants

Now write in the missing vowels in these words too!

 e_lephant

 carr_o_t

 f_i_sh

 fl_o_wer

 b_u_rd

 m_u_sic

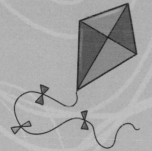 k_i_te

 _u_mbrella

 d_o_ll

 d_o_g

Fill in the vowel letters in your favourite colours.

10

Using vowels

Add the missing vowels to complete each sentence.
Will you need to write a, e, i, o or u?

1. The e_gg is _on the n_e_st.

2. The d_o_g r_u_ns _and j_u_mps.

3. The _a_pple goes cr_u_nch.

4. The f_i_sh sw_i_ms in the r_i_ver.

Draw a picture to go with one sentence.

Double letters

I read lots of books. Look at the words 'book' and 'look'. They both have double letters in them – 'oo'. Say out loud the double letter sounds in the stars below. Match each picture with the correct double letter sound. Now finish each word by writing in the correct double letter sound.

★ oo   ★ ee   ★ ll   ★ ss

ba_ll_

f_oo_d

do_ll_

be_ll_

b_oo_t

b_ee_

m_oo_n

gla_s_s_

tr_ee_

gra_s_s_

dre_s_s_

b_oo_k

More double letters

Write in the missing double letters in these sentences.

Po ll y has a pet ra bb it

ca ll ed Mops, who likes

to eat ca rr ots.

Mia has a cute pu ss y

ca ll ed Dudley.

Her favourite toy is her

li tt le te dd y.

Double doubles

Each word below has two sets of double letters. Write them in the boxes.

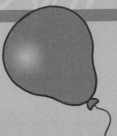 balloon oo and ll

 beekeeper ee and ee

 woolly oo and ll

 toffee ff and ee

 address dd and ss

 happiness pp and ss

14

Sounds the same!

Some words sound the same but are spelt differently, and have a different meaning. These words are called homophones. Look at the words below. Draw lines to match up the words that sound the same. The first one has been done for you. Colour in a petal on the flower for every match you make.

flower   pair

hair   son

see   flour

sun   hare

pear   sea

Two to one

Sometimes two is twice as good as one! Draw a line to match the pairs of words that, put together, make one word.

book   dog

star   fire

sheep   worm

cup   fish

camp   cake

Silent letters

Some words contain silent letters – you can't hear them when you say the word. For example, you can't hear the 'h' in 'school'. Say the words below out loud, then draw a line under the silent letter in each word.

whale

knight

lamb

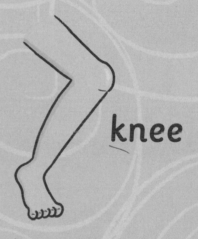

knee

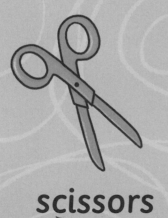

scissors

handkerchief

sword

Add a letter

Sometimes, just adding one letter can make a whole new word!

Use the letters listed below:

l   b   t   w   c   s

sea____   ____hair

____ear   ____hen

____rain   ____wing

Rhyming words

Rhyming words are words that sound the same at the end of the word. For example, 'mouse' and 'house' are rhyming words. Read all these words out loud. Draw lines to match up the words that rhyme.

shower	house
hen	cook
mouse	pen
book	boat
dish	sock
coat	flower
cat	hat
lock	fish

Rhyming words

Read all these words out loud.
Draw lines to match up the words that rhyme.

Use a blue pencil to colour in the two words in each row
that rhyme. Colour the word that doesn't rhyme in red.

fox    bat    rat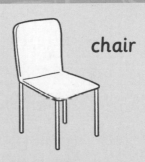

pear    apple    chair

train    rain    sun

shoe 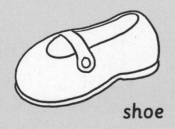   red    blue

Plurals

Hello, I'm Noah. When you have more than one of something it is called a plural. Some plural words can be made by adding 's' or 'es' at the end of the word.

girl   girl**s**   tomato   tomato**es**

Draw a matching picture in the white space of each thing shown, so that there is more than one of each item.

Plurals with 's'

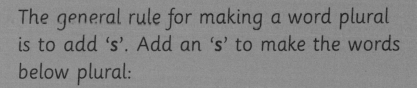

The general rule for making a word plural is to add 's'. Add an 's' to make the words below plural:

flower____   ball____

book____   dog____

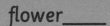

kite____   duck____

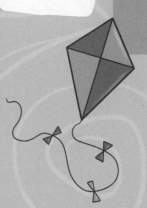

Plurals with 'es'

When a singular word (when there is just one of something) ends in 's', 'x', 'ss', 'ch' or 'sh', you add an 'es' to make it plural.

Draw a matching picture in the white space of each thing shown, so that there is more than one of each item. Then add an 'es' to make the words plural.

fox____ ____   dish____ ____

lunch____ ____   glass____ ____

dress____ ____   kiss____ ____

bus____ ____   sandwich____ ____

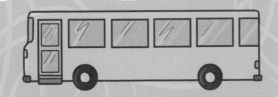

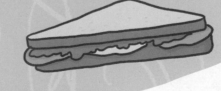

S is the beSt!

Look at the pictures below and then fill in the missing letters. Each one begins and ends with the letter 's'.

s __ __ __ __ s

s __ __ __ __ s

s __ __ __ __ s

s __ __ __ __ __ s

s __ __ __ __ __ __ s

s __ __ __ d w __ __ __ __ __ s

Playing in the park!

I enjoy playing in the park with my friends. We love running, jumping, hopping, skipping, walking and kicking a ball! Sometimes we just like sitting down and looking around us.

Have you noticed that all these action words have 'ing' on the end of them?

Write a word to describe what action each person is doing.

More action words!

Add '**ing**' to complete the action words in each of these sentences.

Joe is read____ ____ ____ a book about animals.

Mia is walk____ ____ ____ her dog, Dudley.

Noah is listen____ ____ ____ to music.

Poppy is feed____ ____ ____ Mops some carrots.

Write a word to describe what action each person is doing.

Even more action words!

I'm ready to have an action-filled weekend of fun!
Fill in the missing words to complete the sentences below.

| fly | hold | eat |

| cook | throw |

I am __ _ __ __ ing a kite.

I am __ __ __ __ __ ing my teddy.

I am __ __ __ ing a cake.

I am __ __ __ __ __ ing a pizza.

I am __ __ __ __ __ __ ing a ball.

What's the sound?

It can be quite tricky to spell words that have these letter sounds in them: 'ch' 'sh' 'th' 'ck'.

church shark thumb clock

Let's practise them together.

Start by saying the sounds out loud so you can hear them clearly.
Then write in the correct letter sound to finish each word.

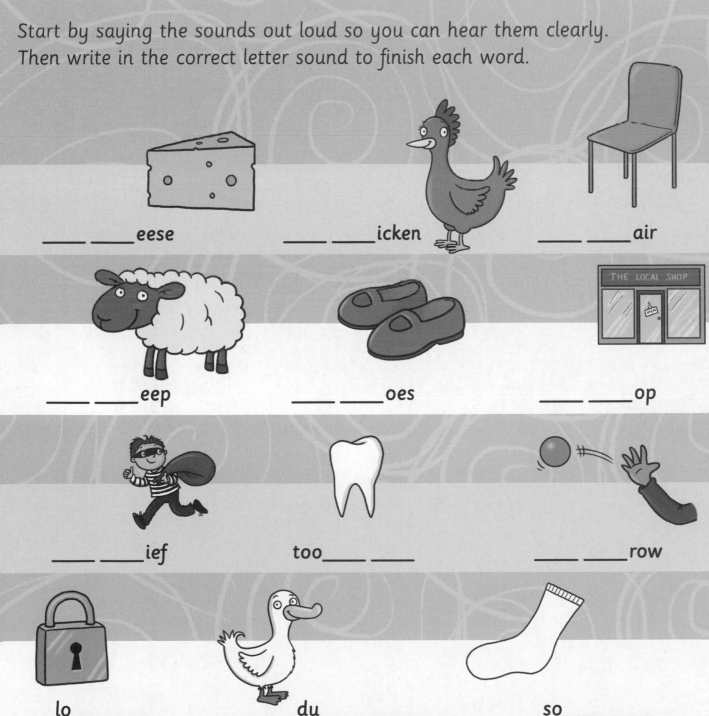

_____ _____eese   _____ _____icken   _____ _____air

_____ _____eep   _____ _____oes   _____ _____op

_____ _____ief   too_____ _____   _____ _____row

lo_____ _____   du_____ _____   so_____ _____

27

Words ending in 'ook'

Lots of words end with the letter sound 'ook'. Finish these words by writing in the missing letter sound.

I read a b ___ ___ ___.

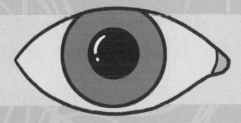

I have food to c ___ ___ ___.

Have a l ___ ___ ___.

The tree sh ___ ___ ___.

The fish is on a h___ ___ ___.

Words containing 'ee'

When I giggle it sounds like 'hee hee'!
Finish each word below by adding the letter sound 'ee'.

tr____ ____

thr____ ____

s____ ____

kn____ ____

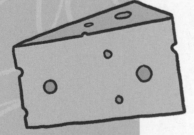

ch____ ____se

b____ ____

Answers

Page 5

jug, egg, dog, boat, bird, orange, hat, boy
Three words start with the letter b – boat, bird, boy.

Page 6

m_um   **s**_ister
d_ad   **g**_randpa
b_rother   **g**_randma

Page 7

do**g**
fo**x**
rabbi**t**
ca**t**
fis**h**
bir**d**
co**w**
pi**g**

Page 8

m_oo   **m**_eow
t_weet   **c**_luck
o_ink   **s**_queak
w_oof   **b**_aa

Page 9

orange, baby, green, apple, pink, hat, yellow, teddy, blue, pen

Page 10

elephant, carrot, fish, flower, bird, music, kite, umbrella, doll, dog

Page 11

1. The **e**_gg is **i**_n the n**e**_st.

2. The d**o**_g r**u**_ns **a**_nd j**u**_mps.

3. The **a**_pple goes cr**u**_nch.

4. The f**i**_sh sw**i**_ms in the r**i**_ver.

Page 12

ball, food, doll, bell, boot, bee, moon, glass, tree, grass, dress, book

Page 13

Po**pp**y has a pet ra**bb**it ca**ll**ed Mops, who likes to eat ca**rr**ots.

Mia has a cute pu**pp**y ca**ll**ed Dudley. Her favourite toy is her li**tt**le te**dd**y.

Page 14

Balloon - **ll** and **oo**
Beekeeper - **ee** and **ee**
Woolly - **oo** and **ll**
Toffee - **ff** and **ee**
Address - **dd** and **ss**
Happiness - **pp** and **ss**

Page 15

flower   pair
hair   son
see   flour
sun   hare
pear   sea

Answers

Page 16

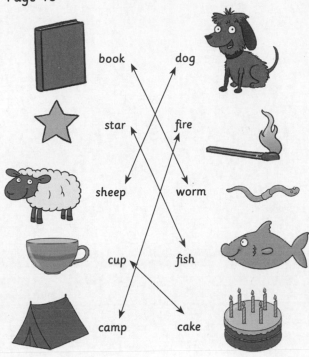

book — dog
star — fire
sheep — worm
cup — fish
camp — cake

Page 17

knight   scissors
whale   handkerchief
lamb   sword
knee

Page 18

seal   chair
bear   when
train   swing

Page 19

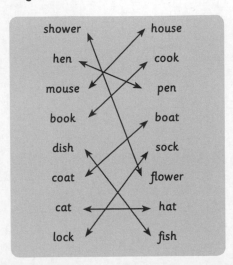

shower — house
hen — cook
mouse — pen
book — boat
dish — sock
coat — flower
cat — hat
lock — fish

Page 20

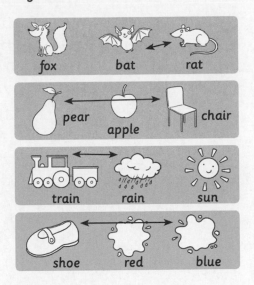

fox   bat   rat

pear   apple   chair

train   rain   sun

shoe   red   blue

Page 21

flowers, balls, books, dogs, kites, ducks

Page 22

foxes, dishes, lunches, glasses, dresses, kisses, buses, sandwiches

Page 23

socks, shoes, stars, snails, sweets, sandwiches

Page 24

eating   reading   skipping

Page 25

reading, walking, listening, feeding

listening   painting   singing

Answers

Page 26

I am __f__ __l__ __y__ ing a kite.

I am __h__ __o__ __l__ __d__ ing my teddy.

I am __e__ __a__ __t__ ing a cake.

I am __c__ __o__ __o__ __k__ ing a pizza.

I am __t__ __h__ __r__ __o__ __w__ ing a ball.

Page 27

cheese, chicken, chair
sheep, shoes, shop
thief, tooth, throw
lock, duck, sock

Page 28

I read a book.

I have food to cook.

Have a look.

The tree shook.

The fish is on a hook.

Page 29

tree

three

see

knee

cheese

bee